Donald's Favorite Season

Advance PUBLISHERS

Advance Publishers, L.C.
1060 Maitland Center Commons, Suite 365
Maitland, FL 32751 USA

10 9 8 7 6 5 4 3 2 1
ISBN-10: 1-57973-388-3

"Hiya, Donald," Mickey said to his pal. "Gee, what's the matter?"
Donald sighed. "Summer and fall are over. There's nothing fun
to do anymore."

"What do you mean?" asked Mickey.

Look up! Hot-air balloons are flying by.

SIGHTSEEING

Hot-air balloons are a great way to see the world from high above.

"Remember in the summer when we went up in the Glove Balloon?" asked Donald.

"Oh, that was fun," Mickey agreed. "We could see for miles!"

"And remember when we went camping and hiking and fishing?" asked Donald.

"You betcha!" said Mickey. "I love summer!"

Donald really likes to hike across different lands.

DIFFERENT KINDS OF LAND

Land, the solid part of the earth's surface, is all around us. Whether as big as a mountain or as small as a backyard, all land is made of the same things: rock, sand, and soil!

NATURE

Fall is here, and there are many changes outdoors. Look! The green leaves on the trees are turning red, orange, and yellow. They are slowly losing their summer green color.

"We did lots of fun things in the fall, too," Donald said. "We planted vegetables and took long bicycle rides."

"That's right," said Mickey. "I remember we had fun jumping in the leaves, too. That was Pluto's favorite!"

Donald shook his head sadly. "But now that's all over. Winter is here, and it's too cold to do any of that stuff anymore."

It's exciting for Donald to watch his seeds grow into vegetables.

SEEDS

First, seeds begin to grow in the soil. With sunshine and water, little green sprouts push their way out! Then they become big plants!

"Summer and fall are great seasons. But there are some things you can only do in the wintertime," Mickey said. "Grab your hat, and I'll show you."

Mickey led Donald outside to the Toon Plane. "I think we're going to need some Mouseketools to help us. 'Oh, Toodles!'"

Toodles arrived with the Mouseketools: a pair of goggles, a cup, and a pillow.

"Which Mouseketool will be helpful in the Toon Plane?" asked Mickey.

"The goggles!" replied Donald.

"Right!" said Mickey. "We've got ears! Say cheers!"

FROST

By the time winter arrives in some parts of the world, autumn's colorful leaves have fallen and the trees are bare. During winter, frost often appears on the grass in the morning.

Mickey and Donald fly over snowy mountains . . .

MOUNTAINS

Some parts of the tundra are called Alpine tundra. The land of the Alpine tundra is filled with huge mountains. These mountain peaks in the Yukon stay covered with snow all year long!

Donald put on the goggles to protect his eyes, and then he and Mickey climbed inside the Toon Plane.

"Where are we going?" Donald asked.

Mickey smiled. "I want to show you how beautiful things look when they are covered in snow."

Donald waved good-bye to their friends as the plane took to the sky. They soared up and over the snowcapped mountains and the snow-covered trees.

"Oh, boy!" exclaimed Donald. "You were right. Everything looks great from up here!"

. . . and icebergs too.

ICEBERGS
Icebergs are often found in the North and South Pole regions, where it is very cold. Newfoundland and Greenland are two countries where you'll see many icebergs.

Now that's cold!

FREEZING
The coldest temperature ever recorded on earth was at the South Pole. It was -128°F.

But before long, Donald began to shiver. "It's really c-c-cold up here."

Mickey shivered, too. "It sure is. And it looks like we're running low on gas."

"Uh-oh!" said Donald.

"I think we have just enough to make it back to the Clubhouse," Mickey said. "Hold on!"

"Brrrr!" said Donald, as Mickey zoomed the plane toward home.

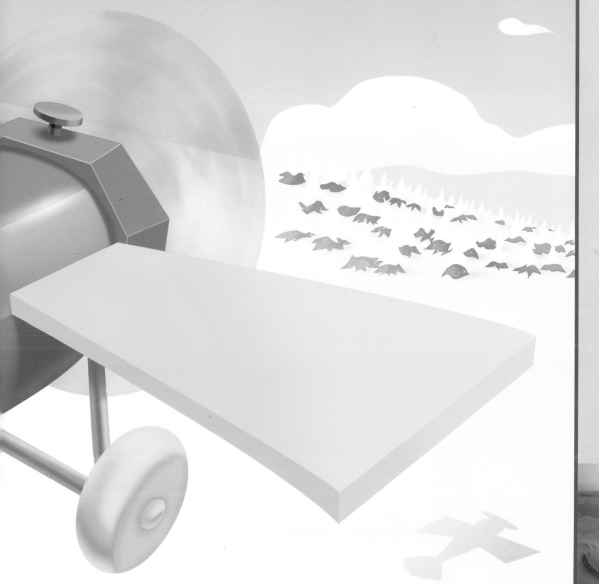

Donald is so cold, he wonders if they are in the tundra!

TUNDRA
The tundra is one of the earth's coldest places.

Donald can't imagine eating only bark all winter!

WINTER

Can you see the needles under the snow? Food becomes scarce in the forest in wintertime, so many animals leave. Some that stay behind will eat tree bark, because they can't find anything else!

Mickey and Donald made it back to the Clubhouse before they ran out of gas.

"I'm sorry it was so cold up there," Mickey told his friend. "I wonder what we can do to warm up?"

"Let's call Toodles," suggested Donald.

"Great idea!" said Mickey.

Toodles rolled over the snow and showed the remaining Mouseketools: a cup and a pillow.

It can be tough going when Mickey and Donald walk in the snow.

WINTER
Animals work harder to find food in the winter.

A fur coat like this comes in handy if you're a fox. But Donald and his friends will have to settle for scarves and hats!

ARCTIC FOXES
Fur on the bottom of its feet help the Arctic fox stay warm.

"Do you think it's the cup?" asked Donald.
"I'll bet a cup of hot chocolate would warm you right up," said Daisy, who was listening nearby.

"We've got ears! Say cheers!" said Mickey. "I love hot chocolate! It's a great treat during the cold wintertime. Thank you, Daisy."

"You're welcome," Daisy said. "And here is some for you, too, Donald."

Donald took a sip of the warm liquid. It tasted good, but he still wasn't convinced that winter could be fun. "I just don't think I'm made for this winter weather," he said.

Donald needs these kinds of feathers to stay warm in the winter.

SNOWY OWLS

When this little snowy owl grows up, its feathers will do something special. They'll turn white! This will help it hide safely in the snow-covered tundra.

Even Donald has to admit that snowflakes are cool.

SNOWFLAKES

Snowflakes are made of tiny drops of water. When it's warm out, the drops of water fall as rain. In the winter, the water drops freeze and turn into tiny ice crystals that fall as snowflakes.

The next morning, there were a few snowflakes coming down, but the friends decided it would be fun to go skating at Star Lake.

"I've never ice-skated before," Donald said nervously.

"How did this ice get here?" asks Donald. "Whoa!"

ICE

Ice is water that has frozen. In very cold temperatures, the water in ponds, lakes, and puddles turns to ice. Ice is smooth and slippery to the touch, and it is usually clear or bluish white.

"Don't worry," said Minnie. "You'll be great."
However, when Donald got out on the ice, he slipped and slid and spun all over the place!
"Whoa! Whoa! Whoa!" he cried.

This looks like a perfect frozen lake for Mickey and his friends to skate on.

FROZEN LAKES
Some lakes stay frozen almost all year long.

"Uh-oh!" exclaimed Goofy. "I think it's time for the last Mouseketool—and fast!"
Goofy took a pillow and quickly placed it beneath Donald, just in time! Donald fell on it, instead of on his bottom.
"Wah!" Donald cried.

"Golly, that was a close call!" said Goofy.
Donald and his friends spent the rest of
the morning skating. By the afternoon, Donald was
actually pretty good. Best of all, he was having fun!

*Donald never noticed
how big icebergs
were before.*

ICEBERGS
You can only see
one-third of an
iceberg above water.

Everyone has fun building a snowman.

SNOW PLAY

Now that it's winter, you'll need to bundle up when you go outside. Put on your hat, your boots, and a heavy winter coat. Don't forget your scarf and mittens!

As the friends left Star Lake, Donald wondered, "What else can we do in the winter?"

"We can build a snowman, we can go snowshoeing, we can go skiing—" began Daisy.

"Let's do them all!" Donald exclaimed.

Mickey gave him a thumbs-up. "Hot dog! Let's go!"

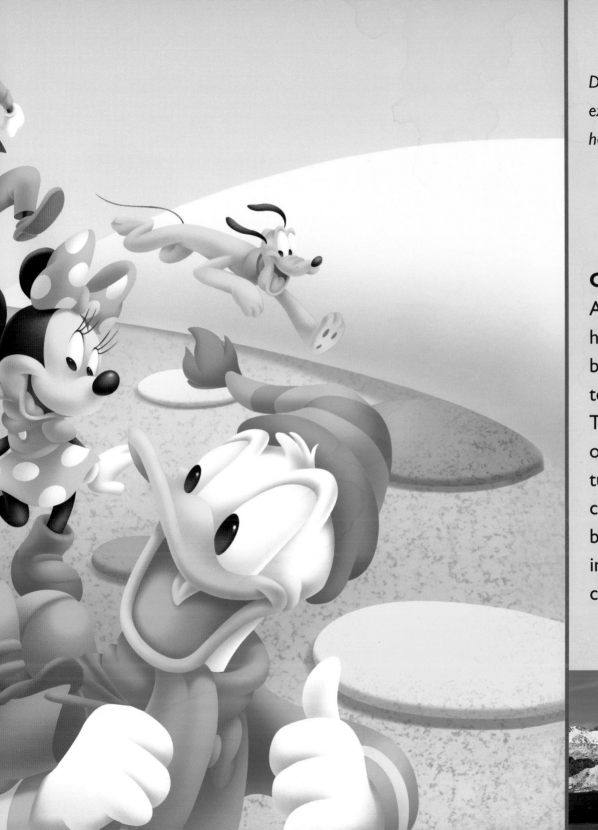

Donald can't wait to go exploring next! Maybe he'll run into a glacier.

GLACIERS

A glacier is like a huge river of ice. It begins as snow on top of a mountain. Then, over thousands of years, the snow turns to ice. Big chunks of ice that break off and fall into the ocean are called icebergs.

It's time for Donald to find some fun things to do in the spring.

SPRING

In some places, spring brings warm, sunny weather.

With all the cool things to do, winter went by quickly. Before long, it was spring.

Mickey noticed his friend was upset. "What's wrong, Donald?"

"I'm sad that winter is over," explained Donald. "It was so much fun!"